7 Minute

Gratitude Journal

-For Kids-

BY: EMMY KOH

This Journal Belongs to:

_____

7 Minute Gratitude Journal for Kids:
30 Days of Practicing Gratitude & Reflection

Copyright © 2020 by Emmy H. Koh

ISBN 978-0-578-67841-2

WHAT IS GRATITUDE?

Gratitude is the feeling of thankfulness we have when someone gives us a present, helps us, or encourages us with words. Did you know that the more we grow our gratitude, the better we usually feel?

One way that we can learn to grow our gratitude is by writing in a gratitude journal like this one. When you write in your journal, you have the chance to think about all of the things that you are thankful for. This is how we practice gratitude! We can be thankful for big things, small things and anything in between.

WHY KEEP A GRATITUDE JOURNAL?

HOW DO I USE THE 7 MINUTE GRATITUDE JOURNAL FOR KIDS?

Fill out the Daily Journal Entry every day by answering the questions on the page. Take your time. And remember, there is no such thing as a wrong answer! Before you start on your first Daily Journal Entry, fill out the "Snapshot in Time" page so that you can remember some of the things you liked and what was happening in the world during the time you were filling out this Journal. Then, after you fill out the very last Daily Journal Entry (Day 30), go on the Gratitude Scavenger Hunt and finish the last page of the Journal by writing a letter to your future self about the things that you learned while journaling.

Date:

A Snapshot in Time

Name: Age:

School: Grade:

MY SELF-PORTRAIT

Why I think it is important to have gratitude:

My Favorite . . .

Memory this year:

Food:

Place to go:

Show:

Song:

Book:

Movie:

Hobby:

Toy:

Daily Journal Entry

TODAY I FEEL (DRAW HOW YOU FEEL TODAY):

CIRCLE THE EMOJI OR EMOJIS THAT SHOW HOW YOU FEEL TODAY:

THE HIGH POINT OF THE DAY WAS . . .

THE LOW POINT OF THE DAY WAS . . .

SOMETHING THAT IS ON MY MIND TODAY IS . . .

TODAY, I AM THANKFUL FOR . . .

1.

2.

TODAY FEELS:

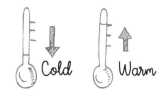

Cold   Warm

THE WEATHER OUTSIDE IS:

I AM GRATEFUL FOR QUIET TIMES TO THINK AND PLAY.

What do you like to do during quiet times in your day? Do you like to draw? Read? Daydream? Write or draw about it below:

Daily Journal Entry

TODAY I FEEL (DRAW HOW YOU FEEL TODAY):

CIRCLE THE EMOJI OR EMOJIS THAT SHOW HOW YOU FEEL TODAY:

THE HIGH POINT OF THE DAY WAS . . .

THE LOW POINT OF THE DAY WAS . . .

SOMETHING THAT IS ON MY MIND TODAY IS . . .

TODAY, I AM THANKFUL FOR . . .

1.

2.

TODAY FEELS:

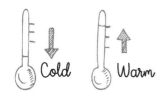

THE WEATHER OUTSIDE IS:

I AM GRATEFUL FOR MY FRIENDS.

Think about a friend who you are grateful for. Write about why he or she is special to you.

Daily Journal Entry

TODAY I FEEL (DRAW HOW YOU FEEL TODAY):

CIRCLE THE EMOJI OR EMOJIS THAT SHOW HOW YOU FEEL TODAY:

THE HIGH POINT OF THE DAY WAS . . .

THE LOW POINT OF THE DAY WAS . . .

SOMETHING THAT IS ON MY MIND TODAY IS . . .

TODAY, I AM THANKFUL FOR . . .

1.

2.

TODAY FEELS:

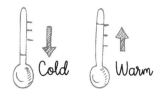

THE WEATHER OUTSIDE IS:

I AM GRATEFUL FOR MY STRENGTHS.

A strength is something that you are good at doing. Can you list some of your strengths below? How can you use these strengths to help others?

Daily Journal Entry

TODAY I FEEL (DRAW HOW YOU FEEL TODAY):

CIRCLE THE EMOJI OR EMOJIS THAT SHOW HOW YOU FEEL TODAY:

THE HIGH POINT OF THE DAY WAS . . .

THE LOW POINT OF THE DAY WAS . . .

SOMETHING THAT IS ON MY MIND TODAY IS . . .

TODAY, I AM THANKFUL FOR . . .

1.

2.

Date:

Day 4

TODAY FEELS:

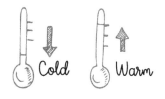

Cold   Warm

THE WEATHER OUTSIDE IS:

I AM GRATEFUL FOR HELPERS.

Write about someone who helped you this week. It could be in a big or small way (e..g., like someone helping you with your homework, or someone sticking up for you when others did not, etc.).

Why do you think that this person helped you? How did you feel when they helped you?

13

Daily Journal Entry

TODAY I FEEL (DRAW HOW YOU FEEL TODAY):

CIRCLE THE EMOJI OR EMOJIS THAT SHOW HOW YOU FEEL TODAY:

THE HIGH POINT OF THE DAY WAS . . .

THE LOW POINT OF THE DAY WAS . . .

SOMETHING THAT IS ON MY MIND TODAY IS . . .

TODAY, I AM THANKFUL FOR . . .

1.

2.

Date:

TODAY FEELS:

THE WEATHER OUTSIDE IS:

I CAN BE GRATEFUL FOR LESSONS I LEARN FROM OBSTACLES.

Sometimes we run into obstacles in life. An obstacle is something that gets in our way, or keeps us from doing something that we want to do. But sometimes we are able to learn from the obstacles we face if we look for a lesson in the situation. Can you think of an obstacle that you faced? What did you learn?

Daily Journal Entry

TODAY I FEEL (DRAW HOW YOU FEEL TODAY):

CIRCLE THE EMOJI OR EMOJIS THAT SHOW HOW YOU FEEL TODAY:

THE HIGH POINT OF THE DAY WAS . . .

THE LOW POINT OF THE DAY WAS . . .

SOMETHING THAT IS ON MY MIND TODAY IS . . .

TODAY, I AM THANKFUL FOR . . .

1.

2.

TODAY FEELS: THE WEATHER OUTSIDE IS:

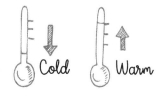

AM GRATEFUL FOR GIFTS AND GIFT GIVERS.

What is a special gift that you received? Write about who gave you the gift, and what made it special.

Can you think of a special gift that you gave to another person? Why was it special and how did it feel to give the gift?

Daily Journal Entry

TODAY I FEEL (DRAW HOW YOU FEEL TODAY):

CIRCLE THE EMOJI OR EMOJIS THAT SHOW HOW YOU FEEL TODAY:

THE HIGH POINT OF THE DAY WAS ...

THE LOW POINT OF THE DAY WAS ...

SOMETHING THAT IS ON MY MIND TODAY IS ...

TODAY, I AM THANKFUL FOR ...

1.

2.

TODAY FEELS:

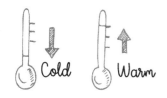

THE WEATHER OUTSIDE IS:

I AM GRATEFUL FOR THE PEOPLE WHO TAKE CARE OF ME.

Who are the people who take care of you every day? What do they help you with? Why are you grateful for them?

Daily Journal Entry

TODAY I FEEL (DRAW HOW YOU FEEL TODAY):

CIRCLE THE EMOJI OR EMOJIS THAT SHOW HOW YOU FEEL TODAY:

THE HIGH POINT OF THE DAY WAS . . .

THE LOW POINT OF THE DAY WAS . . .

SOMETHING THAT IS ON MY MIND TODAY IS . . .

TODAY, I AM THANKFUL FOR . . .

1.

2.

TODAY FEELS:

THE WEATHER OUTSIDE IS:

I AM GRATEFUL FOR FAMILY TRADITIONS.

Does your family have any special traditions? There are a lot of examples of different traditions. For example it can be something that happens every week like Friday pizza night, something that you always do on Thanksgiving, or a special treat you receive for your birthday. Write about it below.

Daily Journal Entry

TODAY I FEEL (DRAW HOW YOU FEEL TODAY):

CIRCLE THE EMOJI OR EMOJIS THAT SHOW HOW YOU FEEL TODAY:

THE HIGH POINT OF THE DAY WAS . . .

THE LOW POINT OF THE DAY WAS . . .

SOMETHING THAT IS ON MY MIND TODAY IS . . .

TODAY, I AM THANKFUL FOR . . .

1.

2.

TODAY FEELS:

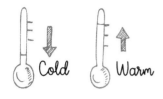

Cold   Warm

THE WEATHER OUTSIDE IS:

I AM GRATEFUL FOR PEOPLE IN HISTORY.

What would life be like if we were not able to turn on the lights, play our favorite video game or watch a television show because there was no electricity? Many people, over many years, studied electricity so that we are able to turn on the lights and use our electronic gadgets. One of the most famous is Benjamin Franklin who conducted a kite experiment and discovered the connection between lightning and electricity. Can you think of another person in history who, like Benjamin Franklin, made the world a better place? Write about this person below and why you are thankful for him or her.

Daily Journal Entry

TODAY I FEEL (DRAW HOW YOU FEEL TODAY):

CIRCLE THE EMOJI OR EMOJIS THAT SHOW HOW YOU FEEL TODAY:

THE HIGH POINT OF THE DAY WAS . . .

THE LOW POINT OF THE DAY WAS . . .

SOMETHING THAT IS ON MY MIND TODAY IS . . .

TODAY, I AM THANKFUL FOR . . .

1.

2.

TODAY FEELS: THE WEATHER OUTSIDE IS:

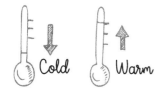

I AM GRATEFUL FOR THE FOOD I EAT.

Have you ever thought about how the food you eat ended up on your dinner table? There are many people who help grow and deliver our food like farmers, food factory workers, and grocery store workers! Think about apples, for example. Farmers grow apples on apple trees, pick them by hand, then send them to a factory where they pack and ship them to supermarkets so that people can buy them. Write about your favorite food and the people who grow, make and sell it.

Make time this week to learn a new fact about the farmers and other workers who make it possible for us to enjoy the delicious foods we eat.

Daily Journal Entry

TODAY I FEEL (DRAW HOW YOU FEEL TODAY):

CIRCLE THE EMOJI OR EMOJIS THAT SHOW HOW YOU FEEL TODAY:

THE HIGH POINT OF THE DAY WAS . . .

THE LOW POINT OF THE DAY WAS . . .

SOMETHING THAT IS ON MY MIND TODAY IS . . .

TODAY, I AM THANKFUL FOR . . .

1.

2.

TODAY FEELS:

Cold   Warm

THE WEATHER OUTSIDE IS:

I AM GRATEFUL FOR THE LESSONS I LEARN FROM FAILURE.

Did you know that Thomas Edison tried over a thousand times before he was able to create a successful storage battery? You might think that Mr. Edison looked at these failures as bad things. But he did not! Instead, every time he failed, he saw it as a chance to learn something new. He famously said: "I have gotten lots of results! I know several thousand things that won't work!" We can learn from our failures too. Write about something that you failed at and what you learned from the situation.

Daily Journal Entry

TODAY I FEEL (DRAW HOW YOU FEEL TODAY):

CIRCLE THE EMOJI OR EMOJIS THAT SHOW HOW YOU FEEL TODAY:

THE HIGH POINT OF THE DAY WAS . . .

THE LOW POINT OF THE DAY WAS . . .

SOMETHING THAT IS ON MY MIND TODAY IS . . .

TODAY, I AM THANKFUL FOR . . .

1.

2.

TODAY FEELS:

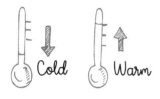

Cold   Warm

THE WEATHER OUTSIDE IS:

I AM GRATEFUL FOR GOOD MEMORIES.

Do you have any special memories about something that you did this year? What did you do? Who were you with? How did it make you feel?

Daily Journal Entry

TODAY I FEEL (DRAW HOW YOU FEEL TODAY):

CIRCLE THE EMOJI OR EMOJIS THAT SHOW HOW YOU FEEL TODAY:

THE HIGH POINT OF THE DAY WAS . . .

THE LOW POINT OF THE DAY WAS . . .

SOMETHING THAT IS ON MY MIND TODAY IS . . .

TODAY, I AM THANKFUL FOR . . .

1.

2.

TODAY FEELS:

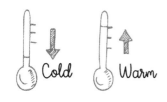

THE WEATHER OUTSIDE IS:

I AM GRATEFUL FOR LAUGHTER.

Sometimes laughter is the best medicine. Laughing can help you calm down when you are nervous, brighten your spirits, and even help you stay healthy! Write about something that makes you belly laugh.

This week, watch a funny show, read a funny book, tell someone a joke, or find another way to laugh out loud.

Daily Journal Entry

TODAY I FEEL (DRAW HOW YOU FEEL TODAY):

CIRCLE THE EMOJI OR EMOJIS THAT SHOW HOW YOU FEEL TODAY:

THE HIGH POINT OF THE DAY WAS . . .

THE LOW POINT OF THE DAY WAS . . .

SOMETHING THAT IS ON MY MIND TODAY IS . . .

TODAY, I AM THANKFUL FOR . . .

1.

2.

TODAY FEELS:

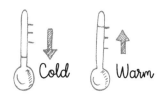

THE WEATHER OUTSIDE IS:

I A GRATEFUL FOR MY EYES, NOSE, EARS, FINGERS AND MOUTH.

Did you know that our eyes can see up to 10 million different colors, our noses can detect at least 1 trillion different smells, our tongues have between 2,000 and 4,000 taste buds, our ears help us to stay balanced, and our fingers can feel a ridge as small as 13 nanometers (about the width of human hair) in size? What sense are you most thankful for, and why?

Daily Journal Entry

TODAY I FEEL (DRAW HOW YOU FEEL TODAY):

CIRCLE THE EMOJI OR EMOJIS THAT SHOW HOW YOU FEEL TODAY:

THE HIGH POINT OF THE DAY WAS . . .

THE LOW POINT OF THE DAY WAS . . .

SOMETHING THAT IS ON MY MIND TODAY IS . . .

TODAY, I AM THANKFUL FOR . . .

1.

2.

TODAY FEELS: THE WEATHER OUTSIDE IS:

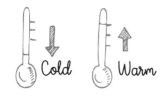 Cold   Warm

I AM GRATEFUL FOR DIFFERENCES BETWEEN PEOPLE.

Every person is unique. And that is a great thing! We have different strengths and see the world in different ways. This is why it is helpful to have different people come together to solve problems. Think about yourself, people in your family, and a couple of your friends. What makes each person unique? Write about how everyone's differences can be a good thing.

Daily Journal Entry

TODAY I FEEL (DRAW HOW YOU FEEL TODAY):

CIRCLE THE EMOJI OR EMOJIS THAT SHOW HOW YOU FEEL TODAY:

THE HIGH POINT OF THE DAY WAS . . .

THE LOW POINT OF THE DAY WAS . . .

SOMETHING THAT IS ON MY MIND TODAY IS . . .

TODAY, I AM THANKFUL FOR . . .

1.

2.

TODAY FEELS:

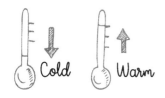

THE WEATHER OUTSIDE IS:

I AM GRATEFUL FOR TIME TO PLAY.

What is your favorite thing to play inside? What is your favorite thing to play outside? What is your favorite toy? Who do you like to play with? Write about it below.

Daily Journal Entry

TODAY I FEEL (DRAW HOW YOU FEEL TODAY):

CIRCLE THE EMOJI OR EMOJIS THAT SHOW HOW YOU FEEL TODAY:

THE HIGH POINT OF THE DAY WAS . . .

THE LOW POINT OF THE DAY WAS . . .

SOMETHING THAT IS ON MY MIND TODAY IS . . .

TODAY, I AM THANKFUL FOR . . .

1.

2.

TODAY FEELS:

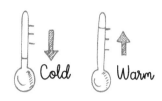

Cold   Warm

THE WEATHER OUTSIDE IS:

I AM GRATEFUL FOR SECOND CHANCES.

Are you grateful for second chances? Your parents may give you a second chance to listen after you didn't listen the first time they asked. A friend may give you a second chance to play even after you did not share a toy with them.   Can you think of a time when someone gave you a second chance? Write about what happened and how it made you feel to get a second chance.

Can you think of a time when you gave someone else a second chance? Write about it below.

Daily Journal Entry

TODAY I FEEL (DRAW HOW YOU FEEL TODAY):

CIRCLE THE EMOJI OR EMOJIS THAT SHOW HOW YOU FEEL TODAY:

THE HIGH POINT OF THE DAY WAS . . .

THE LOW POINT OF THE DAY WAS . . .

SOMETHING THAT IS ON MY MIND TODAY IS . . .

TODAY, I AM THANKFUL FOR . . .

1.

2.

TODAY FEELS:

THE WEATHER OUTSIDE IS:

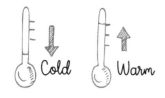

I AM GRATEFUL FOR MY CHORES AND HOMEWORK.

When we do chores at home we help our family and learn how to be responsible. When we work on homework we exercise our minds and learn how to study. What chores and homework did you work on this week? What did you learn?

Daily Journal Entry

TODAY I FEEL (DRAW HOW YOU FEEL TODAY):

CIRCLE THE EMOJI OR EMOJIS THAT SHOW HOW YOU FEEL TODAY:

THE HIGH POINT OF THE DAY WAS . . .

THE LOW POINT OF THE DAY WAS . . .

SOMETHING THAT IS ON MY MIND TODAY IS . . .

TODAY, I AM THANKFUL FOR . . .

1.

2.

TODAY FEELS: THE WEATHER OUTSIDE IS:

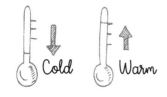

I AM GRATEFUL FOR HOLIDAYS.

What is your favorite holiday to celebrate? Write about why this is your favorite holiday, some things that you do to celebrate and who you are usually with.

Daily Journal Entry

TODAY I FEEL (DRAW HOW YOU FEEL TODAY):

CIRCLE THE EMOJI OR EMOJIS THAT SHOW HOW YOU FEEL TODAY:

THE HIGH POINT OF THE DAY WAS . . .

THE LOW POINT OF THE DAY WAS . . .

SOMETHING THAT IS ON MY MIND TODAY IS . . .

TODAY, I AM THANKFUL FOR . . .

1.

2.

TODAY FEELS:

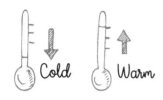

THE WEATHER OUTSIDE IS:

I AM GRATEFUL THAT I CAN HELP OTHERS.

Have you heard the saying that it is better to give than receive? What do you think that this means?

Think of a time when you helped another person, or gave someone a gift. How did that make you feel?

How can you help someone this week?

Daily Journal Entry

TODAY I FEEL (DRAW HOW YOU FEEL TODAY):

CIRCLE THE EMOJI OR EMOJIS THAT SHOW HOW YOU FEEL TODAY:

THE HIGH POINT OF THE DAY WAS . . .

THE LOW POINT OF THE DAY WAS . . .

SOMETHING THAT IS ON MY MIND TODAY IS . . .

TODAY, I AM THANKFUL FOR . . .

1.

2.

TODAY FEELS:

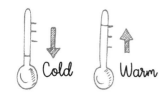

THE WEATHER OUTSIDE IS:

I AM GRATEFUL FOR HEROES.

A hero is someone who does something brave to help another person, even if helping puts himself or herself in danger. Can you think of a famous person from history who is a hero? You may have learned about him or her by reading books, or from your teachers at school. Write about what you admire about this person.

Can you think of someone who may not be famous, but is a hero? Write about what you admire about this person.

Daily Journal Entry

TODAY I FEEL (DRAW HOW YOU FEEL TODAY):

CIRCLE THE EMOJI OR EMOJIS THAT SHOW HOW YOU FEEL TODAY:

THE HIGH POINT OF THE DAY WAS . . .

THE LOW POINT OF THE DAY WAS . . .

SOMETHING THAT IS ON MY MIND TODAY IS . . .

TODAY, I AM THANKFUL FOR . . .

1.

2.

TODAY FEELS: THE WEATHER OUTSIDE IS:

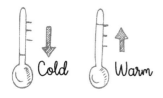

I AM THANKFUL FOR LEARNING.

There are so many things to learn about, and so many ways to learn. Write about something that you had fun learning about. What did you learn and how did you learn it?

Daily Journal Entry

TODAY I FEEL (DRAW HOW YOU FEEL TODAY):

CIRCLE THE EMOJI OR EMOJIS THAT SHOW HOW YOU FEEL TODAY:

THE HIGH POINT OF THE DAY WAS . . .

THE LOW POINT OF THE DAY WAS . . .

SOMETHING THAT IS ON MY MIND TODAY IS . . .

TODAY, I AM THANKFUL FOR . . .

1.

2.

TODAY FEELS:

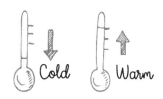

THE WEATHER OUTSIDE IS:

I AM GRATEFUL FOR NATURE.

Did you know that glass is made from sand, and diamonds are made from coal? Or that one tree can make enough oxygen for two people to live off their entire lives? Write about or draw one thing in nature that you are thankful for and why you are describe why you are thankful for it.

Daily Journal Entry

TODAY I FEEL (DRAW HOW YOU FEEL TODAY):

CIRCLE THE EMOJI OR EMOJIS THAT SHOW HOW YOU FEEL TODAY:

THE HIGH POINT OF THE DAY WAS . . .

THE LOW POINT OF THE DAY WAS . . .

SOMETHING THAT IS ON MY MIND TODAY IS . . .

TODAY, I AM THANKFUL FOR . . .

1.

2.

DAY FEELS:

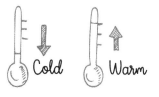

Cold Warm

THE WEATHER OUTSIDE IS:

AM GRATEFUL FOR PEOPLE WHO WORK "BEHIND THE SCENES".

Many people work "behind the scenes" every day to make our
ves safer and better. For example, there are police officers,
irefighters, nurses and doctors who help keep us healthy and
afe. List some "behind the scenes" people who you are
hankful for.

Daily Journal Entry

TODAY I FEEL (DRAW HOW YOU FEEL TODAY):

CIRCLE THE EMOJI OR EMOJIS THAT SHOW HOW YOU FEEL TODAY:

THE HIGH POINT OF THE DAY WAS . . .

THE LOW POINT OF THE DAY WAS . . .

SOMETHING THAT IS ON MY MIND TODAY IS . . .

TODAY, I AM THANKFUL FOR . . .

1.

2.

TODAY FEELS: THE WEATHER OUTSIDE IS:

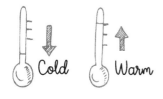   

Cold   Warm

I AM GRATEFUL FOR ACTS OF KINDNESS.

Each one of us can be kind and brighten another person's day.
Write about a time when someone was kind to you. How did it
make you feel?

What are some ways that you can show kindness to someone
this week? List your ideas below and try to do as many things
off of the list that you can this week.

Daily Journal Entry

TODAY I FEEL (DRAW HOW YOU FEEL TODAY):

CIRCLE THE EMOJI OR EMOJIS THAT SHOW HOW YOU FEEL TODAY:

THE HIGH POINT OF THE DAY WAS . . .

THE LOW POINT OF THE DAY WAS . . .

SOMETHING THAT IS ON MY MIND TODAY IS . . .

TODAY, I AM THANKFUL FOR . . .

1.

2.

TODAY FEELS:

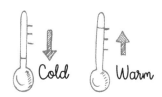

THE WEATHER OUTSIDE IS:

I AM GRATEFUL FOR THE SUNSHINE AND THE RAIN.

Do you love to play outside in the sun? How about jumping in puddles after the rain? The earth needs both sunshine and rain to be healthy. Write about why you are thankful for the sun, rain and all the weather in between. Remember that it takes both rain and sunshine to make a rainbow!

Daily Journal Entry

TODAY I FEEL (DRAW HOW YOU FEEL TODAY):

CIRCLE THE EMOJI OR EMOJIS THAT SHOW HOW YOU FEEL TODAY:

THE HIGH POINT OF THE DAY WAS . . .

THE LOW POINT OF THE DAY WAS . . .

SOMETHING THAT IS ON MY MIND TODAY IS . . .

TODAY, I AM THANKFUL FOR . . .

1.

2.

TODAY FEELS:

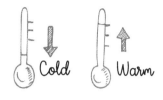

Cold   Warm

THE WEATHER OUTSIDE IS:

AM GRATEFUL FOR MY HOME.

There are many different types of homes. Some people live in a house or an apartment. Others live in a house boat or even a "Tiny House". Draw a picture of your home below. What do you love about your home?

Daily Journal Entry

TODAY I FEEL (DRAW HOW YOU FEEL TODAY):

CIRCLE THE EMOJI OR EMOJIS THAT SHOW HOW YOU FEEL TODAY:

THE HIGH POINT OF THE DAY WAS . . .

THE LOW POINT OF THE DAY WAS . . .

SOMETHING THAT IS ON MY MIND TODAY IS . . .

TODAY, I AM THANKFUL FOR . . .

1.

2.

TODAY FEELS: THE WEATHER OUTSIDE IS:

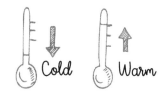

I AM GRATEFUL FOR BOOKS.

Name your favorite book. Write about what it is about and why it is your favorite book to read.

Daily Journal Entry

TODAY I FEEL (DRAW HOW YOU FEEL TODAY):

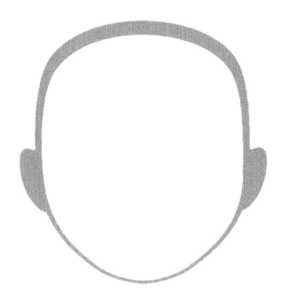

CIRCLE THE EMOJI OR EMOJIS THAT SHOW HOW YOU FEEL TODAY:

THE HIGH POINT OF THE DAY WAS . . .

THE LOW POINT OF THE DAY WAS . . .

SOMETHING THAT IS ON MY MIND TODAY IS . . .

TODAY, I AM THANKFUL FOR . . .

1.

2.

TODAY FEELS:

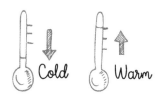

Cold   Warm

THE WEATHER OUTSIDE IS:

I AM GRATEFUL FOR THE COMMUNITIES I BELONG TO.

A community is a group of people who live or work together in the same area. Most of us belong to many different communities. This can include our neighborhood, school, and faith communities. Communities help and support one another. What communities are you a part of? Why you are thankful for each one?

Daily Journal Entry

TODAY I FEEL (DRAW HOW YOU FEEL TODAY):

CIRCLE THE EMOJI OR EMOJIS THAT SHOW HOW YOU FEEL TODAY:

THE HIGH POINT OF THE DAY WAS . . .

THE LOW POINT OF THE DAY WAS . . .

SOMETHING THAT IS ON MY MIND TODAY IS . . .

TODAY, I AM THANKFUL FOR . . .

1.

2.

TODAY FEELS:

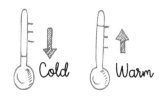

Cold   Warm

THE WEATHER OUTSIDE IS:

I AM GRATEFUL FOR THINGS THAT MAKE ME SMILE.

Did you know that smiles are good for your body? Whenever you smile, your brain releases feel-good chemicals (scientists call these chemicals neurotransmitters) that help you feel happier. Smiles are also contagious! When you smile at someone else, they likely cannot help but smile back. List some things that make you smile below.

Try to smile more this week, and try to make others smile too!

Gratitude Scavenger Hunt

DID YOU KNOW THAT YOU CAN GO ON A GRATITUDE SCAVENGER HUNT EVERY DAY? YOU CAN LOOK FOR REASONS TO BE THANKFUL ANYWHERE YOU ARE! HERE ARE SOME IDEAS TO GET YOU STARTED.

1. Find something that puts a smile on your face.

2. Find an animal outside that is interesting.

3. Find a book that you love to read.

4. Find a person that helps you feel safe.

5. Find something that smells yummy.

6. Find something that is beautiful.

7. Find a song that you love to sing along to.

8. Find a game that you have fun playing.

9. Find something that makes you feel warm and cozy.

10. Find something that you love listening to.

11. Find something that is creative.

12. Find something that makes you laugh.

13. Find something that tastes great.

14. Find someone you love.

15. Find a way to brighten someone else's day!

Dear Older Me:

I finished writing in my 7 Minute Gratitude Journal!
I learned that gratitude is:

Remember to always be grateful for . . .

The most important thing in life is . . .

I hope that you . . .

Sincerely,

_____

Date:_____

Made in the USA
Monee, IL
31 October 2020